In loving memory of Ray Feerick,
the ultimate children's book buff

For our children, Shannon and Quinn,
for being strong, healthy role models,
even though it isn't always easy
We're proud of you ☺

To the Hillenbrand and Naumann families,
for their support and love

First Edition, Published by Mitch Spinach Productions, Inc.

Printed in the United States
ISBN 978-0-578-06097-2

Library of Congress Control Number:
2010908922

The Secret Life of Mitch Spinach

by Hillary Feerick & Jeff Hillenbrand
in collaboration with Joel Fuhrman, M.D.

illustrated by Andrea Vitali

Mitch Spinach Productions, Inc.

At 11:45 on an ordinary Tuesday, Ms. Radicchio's class was just settling down for lunch in the noisy cafeteria of Sunchoke Elementary.

Riley, Kayla, Logan, and Nicolas had their usual: chicken fingers and French fries; Lucy, Isabella, Max, and Morgan had their favorite: pepperoni pizza; and Gabrielle, Sara, and Kiera were quietly munching on cream cheese sandwiches and chips taken from their matching rock-star lunchboxes.

Mitch Spinach was unpacking his battery-powered blender and consulting a note that appeared to the other kids to be written in some sort of code.

Mitch Spinach deciphered it in his head, murmuring softly to himself and causing everyone at the table to stare wide-eyed at their unusual classmate. The note read:

Once again, I need your help. Something strange is going on in the janitor's closet! For two mornings now, Mr. Habanero has come in to find his cleaning supplies strewn all over the floor. Someone must be playing a prank, but we don't know who is responsible. Mr. Habanero is spending half of the day cleaning up the mess instead of cleaning up the school. Sunchoke Elementary needs you, Mitch Spinach!

Sincerely,

Your Principal, Mr. Lycopene

4

Mitch Spinach tucked the note back into a tiny pocket on the front of his oversized lunchbox. It had been custom-made by Mitch Spinach, himself, and had 14 different compartments. He called it The Nutripak.

One half of the pack was under temperature-controlled refrigeration and housed a jug of purified water, a jar of flax seeds, and a variety of organic fruits and vegetables. The other half held his homemade super bars, a huge selection of organic nuts and seeds, and three shiny, stainless steel shakers.

6

"What are you putting in your smoothie today, Mitch?" shouted Logan above the din of the lunchroom.

"My favorite, delicious spinach, of course. It super-charges the growth of your muscles and makes you extremely strong," Mitch Spinach said loudly.

The kids weren't surprised. Mitch Spinach could climb to the top of the rope in the gym in under ten seconds. He was amazing!

"Next, I need to add two sweet carrots for super night-vision... you know, to help me see in the dark."

"Seeing in the dark would really come in handy sometimes," said Lucy.

"And we've got to feed the brain, of course," said Mitch Spinach.

"Feed the brain... how do you do that?" asked Kiera.

"Well, certain foods can actually make you smarter and think more clearly."

"No way!" said Kiera. "I never knew that."

"And so, to help me solve any problem that comes my way today, I am going to add a handful of fresh broccoli and one tablespoon of flax seeds. Ah, yummy brain food! For supersonic hearing, I'll use some kiwi, a frozen mango, and a banana, fruits that have what you might call magic powers. One time, I accidentally heard my next-door neighbor talking on the telephone inside his house," said Mitch Spinach.

"Super-sonic hearing from eating fruits and veggies? Awesome!" said Isabella.

Like a Hibachi chef, Mitch Spinach took out the shiny containers, flipped them up in the air, and sprinkled some of each into the blender.

"The icing on the cake," said Mitch Spinach with a smile, and he turned on the blender and mixed all of the powerful ingredients together.

"That looks really good," remarked Nicolas.

"Oh, believe me, it is. AND it's really good for you," said Mitch Spinach, pulling out a gigantic blue and white striped straw from a hidden compartment in his Nutripak and sticking it into the middle of the blender.

He slurped up the super smoothie

in a matter of seconds.

A few moments later, the lunch bell rang, and Ms. Radicchio's class packed up their lunchboxes, threw out their garbage, and formed a single line to head back to class.

Inside the classroom, Ms. Radicchio grabbed her keys to prepare to take her class to recess. "Is everyone ready to go outside and play?" asked Ms. Radicchio.

"Yeah!" screamed all of the kids.

"Wait! Where is Mitch Spinach?" asked Gabrielle.

The kids looked around the room. Mitch Spinach was nowhere to be found.

"That's weird," exclaimed Nicolas. "He was just in the cafeteria with us making one of those incredible super smoothies."

"Mitch Spinach was called to Principal Lycopene's office again," said Ms. Radicchio. "He will have to miss recess today."

"I bet this has something to do with that odd note he was reading," whispered Isabella to Max. "What do you think he did?"

Max just shrugged his shoulders. He couldn't imagine Mitch Spinach doing anything against the rules.

While lining up, all of the children in Ms. Radicchio's class wondered how Mitch Spinach managed to land himself in Mr. Lycopene's office once again. He seemed like an ordinary kid. After all, he was the smartest, nicest kid in the class; he never got into trouble—at least not that anyone ever saw.

Meanwhile, Mitch Spinach was running as fast as he could across the school campus. He had forty-five minutes to solve the mystery and get back to class before recess was over. The janitor's closet was on the opposite side of Sunchoke Elementary. It would have taken a typical student eight minutes to get there, but Mitch Spinach could make it in four minutes flat. Fueled by his super smoothie, Mitch Spinach arrived at the janitor's closet just as Mr. Habanero and Principal Lycopene were unlocking the door.

"Thanks for helping out, Mitch Spinach," exclaimed Mr. Habanero.

"Don't thank me just yet," replied Mitch Spinach. "I haven't solved the mystery."

"Oh, but you will," said Mr. Lycopene. "I can always count on you in these tricky situations."

Mitch Spinach smiled and even blushed a little. He began by examining the closet door lock and then stepped inside.

"It doesn't appear that anyone has tampered with the lock," remarked Mitch Spinach.

"But then how would someone get in?" asked Mr. Lycopene. "Mr. Habanero has the only key."

"Maybe the someone is already inside," whispered Mitch Spinach.

"Ohhh," Mr. Habanero and Mr. Lycopene said simultaneously, as quietly as they could.

Mitch Spinach scanned the closet for clues. Scattered boxes, brooms, and mops littered the floor. He studied the mess of paint and cleaning supplies.

"Hmm," said Mitch Spinach, raising an eyebrow and scratching his chin as he took a closer look at some of the spilled paint.

"Do you know who it could be?" asked Mr. Habanero. "I need to have a few words with that little rascal."

"Shhh," hushed Mitch Spinach. "Do you hear that?"

"Hear what?" said Principal Lycopene.

"I don't hear anything," retorted Mr. Habanero.

"That scratching noise. Shhh!" whispered Mitch Spinach. Mitch Spinach pointed to a small space between two ceiling tiles. "It is coming from up there."

Neither Principal Lycopene nor Mr. Habanero had heard a thing, but both knew Mitch Spinach could hear what no one else could. Before they knew it, Mitch Spinach had found a rope in the corner of the closet, thrown it up toward the space in the ceiling, tied it off, and started climbing straight up with the skill and strength of a monkey. When Mitch Spinach reached the top, he stuck his head through the opening.

"Do you need a flashlight?" Mr. Habanero called. "It must be pitch black up there."

"No thanks. With all the carrots I eat, I can see in the dark... just like your mischievous mess-makers."

Holding on to the rope with one hand and reaching through the ceiling with the other, Mitch Spinach grabbed a large, orange and white cat and two tiny kittens.

He tucked the feline family under his arm and carefully climbed down the rope.

"Here are your little rascals, Mr. Habanero," said Mitch Spinach.

Mr. Habanero's face softened when he saw the mama cat and her kittens.

"Don't be too hard on them," grinned Mitch Spinach.

Mr. Habanero sighed and scratched the kittens behind their ears. "They must have come in during the day through the open door and hidden up there. The mama cat probably tried to find food at night but only ended up making a mess. Mrs. Habanero has been begging me to get her a cat; maybe I should take them home with me."

"That sounds like a great idea," beamed Mitch Spinach.

Principal Lycopene agreed.

"You are incredible, Mitch Spinach," commended Mr. Lycopene. "How did you know to look in the ceiling tiles?"

"Well, since the lock had not been tampered with, I figured that the culprit might actually be locked in instead of having broken in.

The paw prints in the spilled paint and

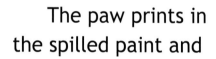

the scratching noise in the ceiling confirmed my suspicion that the guilty party was nothing more than an animal."

"You saw paw prints in the paint? Unbelievable! You are truly an extraordinary kid, Mitch Spinach!"

"Happy to be of service, Principal Lycopene," said Mitch Spinach. "Call on me anytime. I am always ready to help."

And with a bright smile and a quick wave, Mitch Spinach raced back to Room 201 where his classmates were just returning from recess.

Mitch Spinach blended in to the end of the line and found his seat at the back of the classroom.

"Nice to have you back, Mitch Spinach," said Ms. Radicchio. "We missed you at recess."

All of the students spun around in their seats, surprised to see Mitch Spinach calmly sitting in his chair in the back. No one had even seen him enter the classroom. Everyone knew then that Mitch Spinach was no ordinary kid.

Ms. Radicchio just smiled at him and told her students to take out their math books to begin their next lesson.

Later that day at Power Foods Market, while stocking up on dinosaur kale, goji berries, chia seeds, pomegranates, avocado, and wheat grass, Mitch Spinach's mom asked how his day was.

"Great, Mom. I learned a lot about problem solving today. Oh, and by the way, we need more spinach."

His mother smiled and said, "I'm so proud that you understand the importance of eating well."

"I do, Mom—more than you know."

SECRETS FOR PARENTS AND TEACHERS

After reading this book, children ask "Does spinach really make you strong?" or "Do flax seeds make you smarter?" These and other questions provide a great opportunity to explore the teaching message implicit in the Mitch Spinach mission:

Natural plant foods contain necessary and even essential components that enable optimal function of the human body, ensure maximum performance, and prevent against disease.

Do spinach and other green vegetables enhance muscle function?

Because spinach and other dark greens are high in protein and calcium they play an important role in maintaining healthy muscles, bones, and tissues. Furthermore, when protein intake comes more from greens and less from animal products, the body acquires many additional important antioxidants and phytochemicals not present in animal products: nutrients necessary for healthy blood vessels and protection against all diseases, including cancer and dementia. These micronutrients present in greens increase performance during high intensity exercise and increase one's ability to repair muscle, according to a recent study published in the *International Journal of Sport Nutrition and Exercise Metabolism*.

Greens are Rich in Protein and Calcium

PER 100 CALORIES	PROTEIN (gm)	CALCIUM (mg)
Broccoli	11	118
Spinach	13	592
Kale	7	257
Romaine Lettuce	7	194
Roast Sirloin	6	2
Whole Milk	5	189

Do carrots enhance vision?

During World War II, the British Royal Air Force invented the myth tying carrots to clear, sharp vision. A disinformation campaign spread the rumor that British fighter pilots were eating carrots to improve their vision, when in reality the British had a new radar system they wanted to keep secret from Germany. The story caught on, though, and it remains popular to this day. Although there is some truth to the claim, most people will not experience positive changes in their vision from eating carrots unless they have a vitamin A deficiency.

Carrots are, in fact, nutritional heroes; they store a goldmine of nutrients. No other vegetable or fruit contains as much beta carotene, which the body converts to Vitamin A, a crucial nutrient for maintaining proper eyesight. An excellent source of potassium, folate, B vitamins, Vitamin C, and pectin, a type of fiber that lowers cholesterol, the carrot is a truly versatile vegetable.

Can eating fruits and vegetables improve hearing?

Hearing loss is the most common sensory disorder in the United States, affecting more than 36 million people. Eating foods rich in folate protects against developing hearing loss with aging. High folate foods include vegetables such as spinach, asparagus, lettuces, beans and peas, as well as sunflower seeds and fruits, such as mango, kiwi, and banana.

How do broccoli and flax seeds enhance brain function?

Broccoli and its green siblings accelerate the brain to a higher and healthier level of activity. New research finds that the magnesium and other nutrients contained in broccoli and leafy greens not only boost memory and brain power but also ward off the effects of aging on both the brain and the blood vessels. Isothyocyanates (ITC's) in green vegetables control free radical production and protect against atherosclerosis, the major cause of mental decline in the modern world. Greens are also rich in boron, a trace element important in the absorption of calcium and an enhancer of the electrical activity of the brain.

Nuts and seeds like flax are rich in alpha linolenic acid (ALA), omega-3 fats, and other important nutrients for the brain. The body can convert this short-chain omega-3 fat into EPA and DHA, used to make and repair brain cells. If the brain is deprived of the omega-3 essential fats, its neural communication becomes inefficient and delayed, causing memory problems, disorders in mood, and learning difficulties. The lignans (extremely prevalent in flax) and antioxidants in seeds and nuts improve immune function and resistance to disease and prevent cancer later in life.

SOME SECRETS ABOUT A FEW OF THE CHARACTERS IN THIS BOOK

Principal Lycopene is named after a very efficient antioxidant that can neutralize oxygen-derived free radicals. The oxidative damage caused by these free radicals has been linked to many degenerative diseases, such as cardiovascular diseases, premature aging, cancer, and cataracts. Lycopene is generally known for its protective action against prostate cancer. Responsible for the red pigment of tomatoes, lycopene is also found in guava, pink grapefruit, and watermelon.

Ms. Radicchio is named after a burgundy leafed vegetable said to be native to Italy. It is often used in salads and has a crunchy, nutty, pleasantly bitter taste that mellows when cooked. Radicchio is a rich source of dietary fiber, antioxidants, vitamins, and minerals.

Mr. Habanero is named after one very hot pepper. Said to have gotten its name from Havana, Cuba, the habanero pepper, especially the Red Savina variety, is considered the hottest pepper in the world! The habanero ripens from green to yellow, then orange, and finally red at its hottest. Research has shown that hot peppers have high antioxidant and anti-inflammatory properties.

Sunchoke Elementary is named after the sunchoke, a root vegetable native to North America. The main carbohydrate in the sunchoke is inulin that is broken down by bacteria in the gut to form short-chain fatty acids that have been shown to have beneficial health effects. Also called the Jerusalem artichoke, the sunchoke is high in iron, calcium, riboflavin, vitamin B6, vitamin C, and phosphorous. It makes a delicious addition to salads, salsas, marinades, and soups.

The Mitch Spinach
Super Smoothie
(serves 1-2)

INGREDIENTS

2 ounces spinach

1 carrot or 2 to 3 baby carrots

3 to 4 florets broccoli

1 tablespoon flax seeds or ground flax seeds

1 kiwi

6 cubes frozen mango

1 banana

1 teaspoon goji berries

1 teaspoon chia seeds

1 tablespoon *Mitch Spinach Secret Power Powder*
(or similar green powder)

1 cup unsweetened hemp, soy or almond milk

DIRECTIONS

Blend all ingredients together in a high-powered blender until smooth. **Enjoy!**

For more great recipes, nutrition information, games, and Mitch Spinach secrets go to

www.MitchSpinach.com